Money Around the World

Using Money

Rebecca Rissman

H www.heinemannlibrary.co.uk
Visit our website to find out more information about Heinemann Library books.

To order:
☎ Phone +44 (0) 1865 888066
▤ Fax +44 (0) 1865 314091
▣ Visit www.heinemannlibrary.co.uk

Heinemann Library is an imprint of Capstone Global Library Limited, a company incorporated in England and Wales having its registered office at 7 Pilgrim Street, London, EC4V 6LB – Registered company number: 6695582

"Heinemann" is a registered trademark of Pearson Education Limited, under licence to Capstone Global Library Limited
Text © Capstone Global Library Limited 2009
First published in hardback in 2009

Edited by Rebecca Rissman, Siân Smith, and Charlotte Guillain
Designed by Kimberly Miracle and Joanna Malivoire
Picture research by Tracy Cummins
Originated by Capstone Global Library
Printed and bound in China by Leo Paper Products Ltd

ISBN 978 0 431 19428 8 (hardback)
13 12 11 10 09
10 9 8 7 6 5 4 3 2 1

British Library Cataloguing in Publication Data
Rissman, Rebecca.
  Using money. -- (Acorn plus)
  1. Consumption (Economics)--Juvenile literature.
  I. Title II. Series
  339.4'7-dc22

Acknowledgements
The author and publishers are grateful to the following for permission to reproduce copyright material: Age Fotostock p.**20** (© Flying Colours Ltd); Alamy p.**9** (© JLImages); Getty Images pp.**4** (© Lifesize/Brand New Images), **5 right** (© Taxi/Zubin Shroff), **7** (© The Image Bank/Livia Corona), **8** (© Iconica/Andersen Ross), **10** (© Purestock), **15** (© Keith Brofsky), **16 left** (© Photodisc/Alberto Coto), **17** (© Salah Malkawi), **18** (© Gallo Images/Shaen Adey), **19** (© Photographer's Choice/Hugh Sitton), **21 right** (© Nick Dolding); Photolibrary pp.**6** (© Blend Images RF/DreamPictures/Pam Ostrow), **11** (© Digital Vision/PNC PNC), **16 middle** (© Index Stock Imagery/Barry Winiker), **16 right** (© Blend Images RF/Ariel Skelley), **22 left** (© Digital Vision/PNC PNC), **22 right** (© Radius Images); Shutterstock pp.**5 left** (© David Gilder), **12** (© Lena Bernatsky), **13** (© Vincent Giordano), **14** (© Tischenko Irina); The World Bank p.**21 left** (© Eric Miller).

Front cover photograph reproduced with permission of Age Fotostock (© Michel Renaudeau). Back cover photograph reproduced with permission of Getty Images (© Lifesize/Brand New Images).

We would like to thank Nancy Harris and Adriana Scalise for their help in the preparation of this book.

Every effort has been made to contact copyright holders of any material reproduced in this book. Any omissions will be rectified in subsequent printings if notice is given to the publisher.

Contents

What is money?. 4

Wants and needs. 8

Different types of money 12

Getting money 16

Saving money 20

A want or a need? 22

Words to know 23

Index 24

Notes for parents and teachers 24

Some words are shown in bold, **like this**. They are explained in "Words to know" on page 23.

What is money?

Money is something we use to **trade**. We give people money to get things.

We **exchange** money for things. There are different types of money.

Money can be used to buy things. We **spend** money to buy things.

We can sell things for money. We **earn** money when we sell things.

Wants and needs

We use money when we need things. We **spend** money on things we need.

Needs are things that we must have in order to live. We must have food, water, and shelter.

We use money when we want things. We **spend** money on things we want.

Wants are things that we do not need in order to live. Toys, music, and jewellery are wants.

Different types of money

People use different types of money. Coins are small, round pieces of metal. Coins are money. Different countries may use different coins.

Notes are rectangles of paper. Notes are money.
Different countries may use different notes.

Credit cards and **debit cards** are small pieces of plastic. Credit cards and debit cards can be used like money. Different countries may use different types of credit cards and debit cards.

Cheques are pieces of paper that people write on. Cheques can be used like money. Different countries may use different types of cheques.

Getting money

People work to **earn** money. People work at different jobs.

People are paid money to work at jobs. People are given a **wage** for work.

Some people work selling **goods** to **earn** money. Goods are things we eat or use.

Some people work selling **services** to earn money.
Services are jobs people do for others.

Saving money

People can save money for later. Saving money means not **spending** it. Saving money means putting it somewhere safe.

People can save money in banks. People can save money in money boxes. People can save money to buy something special!

A want or a need?

Which picture shows a **want**?
Which picture shows a **need**?

Answer on page 24.

Words to know

cheque   paper that people write on and use like money

credit card   plastic card used like money

debit card   plastic card used like money

earn   to get money for work you have done

exchange   swap

goods   things we eat or use

needs   what people must have. Food, clothing, and shelter are needs.

service   a job people do for others

spend   to use money to get something

trade   to give something in order to get something else

wage   money people get for work they have done

wants   what people do not need. We do not need toys, holidays, or TVs but we do want them.

Index

note 13

card 14, 23

cheque 15, 23

coin 12

goods 18, 23

needs 9, 22, 23

save 20, 21

sell 7, 18, 19

service 19, 23

wants 11, 22, 23

work 16, 17, 18, 19

Notes for parents and teachers

Before reading

Ask the children if they know what money is. How do people get money? After the children respond, tell them that money is something we use to trade to get things we need or want. People earn money by working or selling things. Ask the children if they have ever earned money. Tell the children that there are different types of money. People can also use plastic credit cards or paper cheques when they need to pay for things. Ask the children if they have ever seen a credit card or a cheque.

After reading

- Discuss the difference between selling goods and selling services. Make a list with the children of different ways people can earn money. As the list is being created, ask if each job relates to goods or services.

- Set up a role-play area as a work place such as a supermarket with cashiers, managers, delivery people, and shoppers. Encourage the children to play in role and to use play money to pay for goods and services.

Answer to question on page 22

The picture of someone looking at jewellery shows a want.

The picture of someone buying food shows a need.